Playing in Keys for Viola

Book One:

C, G, and F major

by Cassia Harvey

CHP343

Playing in C Major

Cassia Harvey

A key is like a language: every key contains certain notes and has certain rules.

The key of C major contains all the natural notes on the viola.

There are no sharps or flats in C major.

The notes in the key of C major are all of the notes in the C major scale,
so we will start by learning the notes in the C major scale that occur in first position.

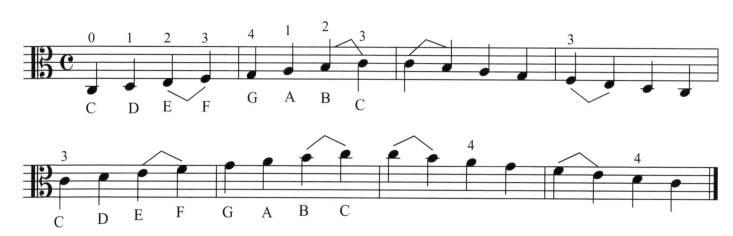

On the viola, the key of C major uses high 2nd finger on the C and G strings
and low 2nd finger on the D and A strings.

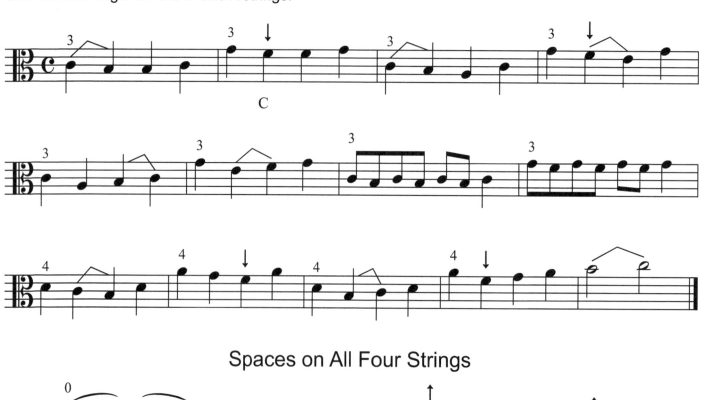

Spaces on All Four Strings

Fra Tante Angoscie

Caraffa, arr. Harvey

The French Assembly

Trad., arr. Harvey

Second Finger Across Strings

C Major Patterns

March

Handel, arr. Harvey

C Major Study No. 1

Maccarony Dance

Trad., arr. Harvey

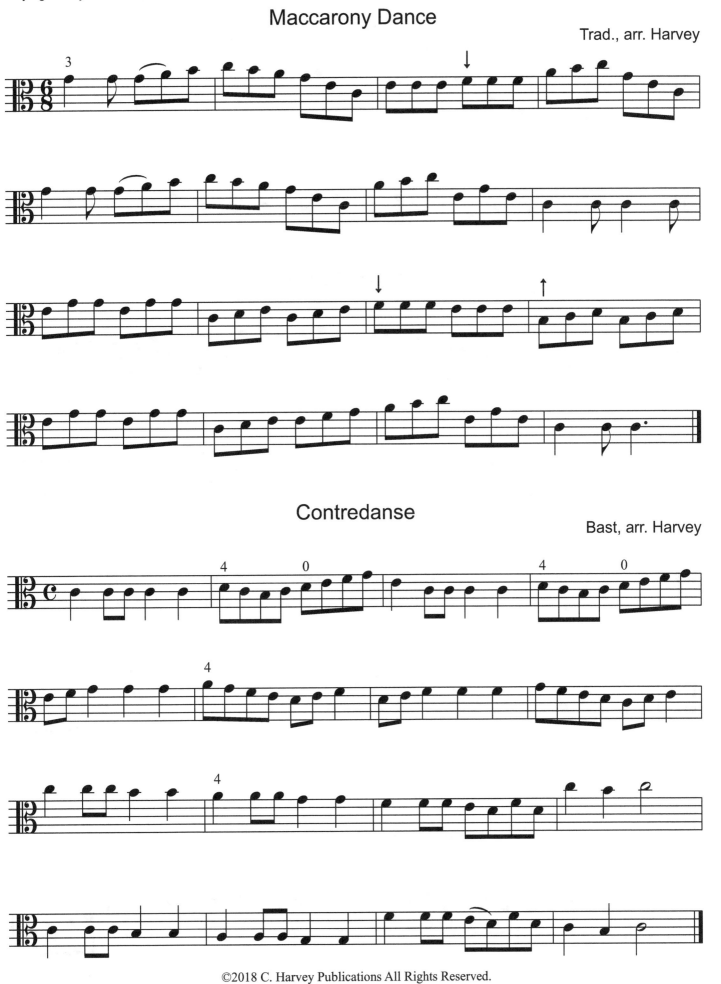

Contredanse

Bast, arr. Harvey

Crossing Strings

C Major Study No. 2

Bonne Bonche

Trad., arr. Harvey

Theme From String Quartet, Op. 77

Haydn, arr. Harvey

Broken Thirds in C Major

Interval Study No. 1

Hornpipe

Trad.., arr. Harvey

Broken Fourths in C Major

Interval Study No. 2

Berlin Waltz

Trad., arr. Harvey

Allegretto

Kling, arr. Harvey

Broken Fifths in C Major

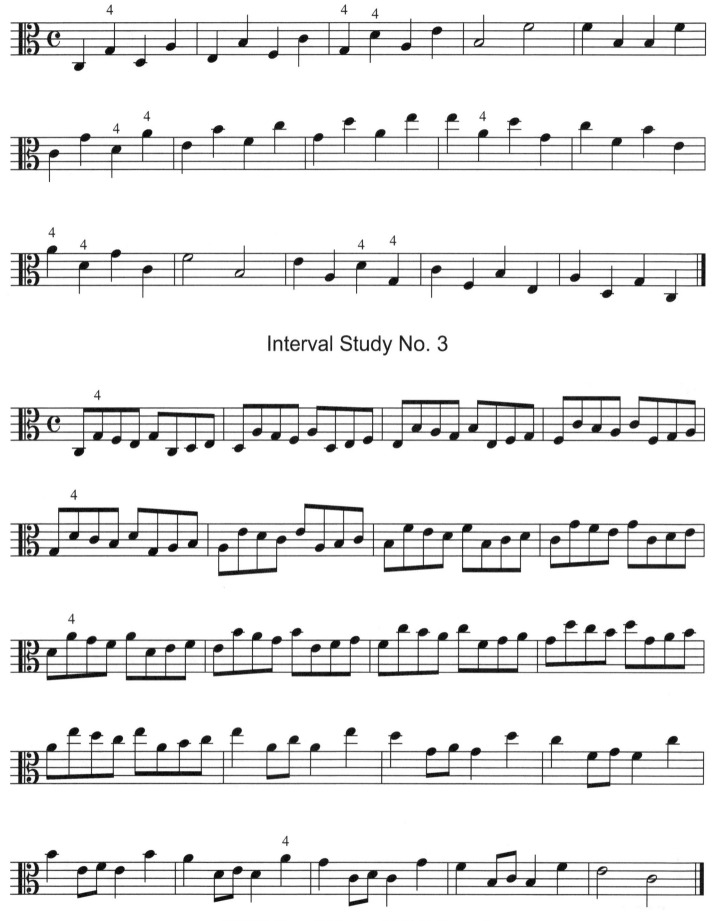

Interval Study No. 3

Scarf Dance

Trad., arr. Harvey

The Devil Among the Tailors

Trad., arr. Harvey

Broken Sixths and Sevenths in C Major

Broken Octaves in C Major

Quick Step

Trad., arr. Harvey

The Notes in G Major

G Major Patterns

A Trip to Stratford Upon Avon

Caraffa, arr. Harvey

Quirky Dance

Trad., arr. Harvey

D Major Study No. 1

High and Low 2nd Fingers in G Major

A Mock Address to the French King

Corbett, arr. Harvey

2nd Fingers Across Strings

G Major Study No. 2

Overture to "The Deserter"

Monsigny, arr. Harvey

Hornpipe

Aldridge, arr. Harvey

Reaching High 3rd Finger F♯

F♯ on the C String

Hearing F♯

French Tune

Trad., arr. Harvey

Cavatine from the Marriage of Figaro

Mozart, arr. Harvey

Finger Patterns on Each String

G Major Study No. 3

Over the Rolling Hills

Harvey

A Stately Minuet

Harvey

Reaching Across to High 3rd Finger

G Major Study No. 4

Schneemann

Struth, arr. Harvey

The Fairy Dance Reel

Trad., arr. Harvey

Crossing Strings

D Major Study No. 5

Fairy Revels Jig

Trad., arr. Harvey

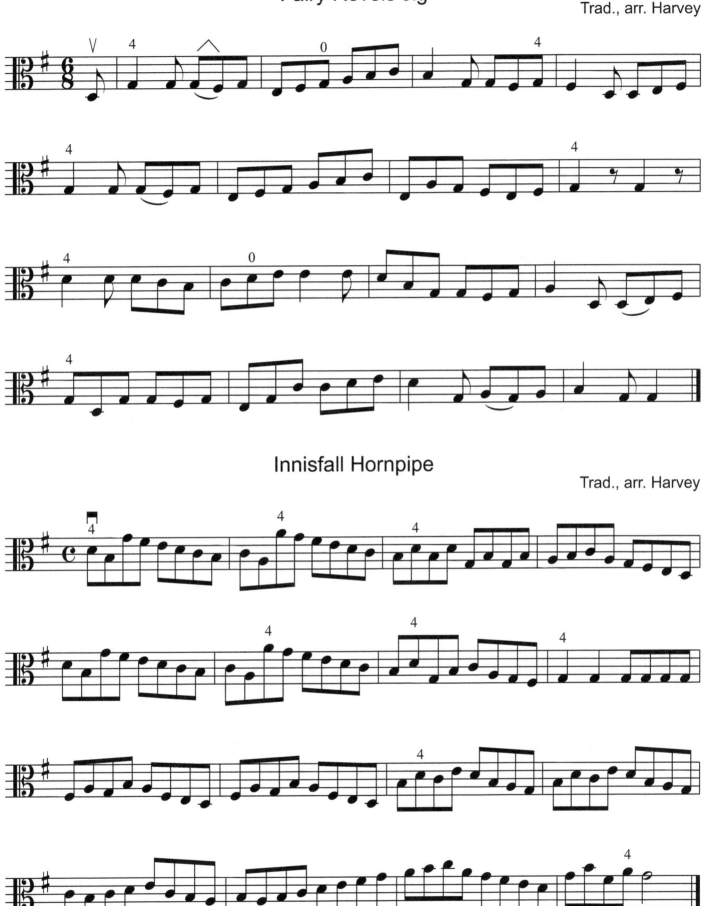

Innisfall Hornpipe

Trad., arr. Harvey

D Major Study No. 6

D Major Study No. 7

Parisott's Hornpipe

Trad., arr. Harvey

Valse de Paris

Trad., arr. Harvey

The Notes in F Major

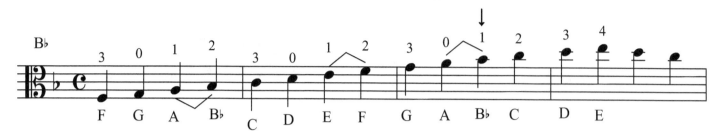

F Major on Each String

Air

Handel, arr. Harvey

The Firefly

Bensley., arr. Harvey

F Major Across Strings

F Major Finger Exercise

Aurora Borealis

Harvey

Within Reason

Harvey

F Major Patterns

F Major Study No. 1

Aiken Drum

Trad., arr. Harvey

Rondeau

Buononcini, arr. Harvey

Switching from High to Low 2nd Finger

Switching to Low B♭ on the A String

Tyrolienne

Rossini, arr. Harvey

Tambourin

Gluck, arr. Harvey

F Major Study No. 4

Reaching Across to Low First Finger on E

A Song Tune

Purcell, arr. Harvey

March in F

Purcell, arr. Harvey

F Major Study No. 5

Gavotta

Purcell, arr. Harvey

F Major Scale Patterns

F Major Study No. 6

Polly Cleveland's Favorite

Trad., arr. Harvey

The Ranting Highlandman

Trad., arr. Harvey

F Major Study No. 7

F Major Study No. 8

Arlequin Marie Sa Fille

Trad., arr. Harvey

The Wedding Ring

Trad., arr. Harvey

Switching Keys; Be Careful!

The Downfall of Paris in C Major

Trad., arr. Harvey

The Downfall of Paris in G Major

Trad., arr. Harvey

The Downfall of Paris in F Major

Trad., arr. Harvey

Flying Fiddle Duets for Two Violas, Book Two

The Frog's Courting

Trad., arr. Myanna Harvey

Made in United States
Troutdale, OR
11/01/2024

24322403R00031